1ST TROMBONE

STANDARD OF EXCELLE

Jazz Ensemble Method

FOR GROUP OR INDIVIDUAL INSTRUCTION

BY DEAN SORENSON & BRUCE PEARSON

Dear Student:

Welcome to the STANDARD OF EXCELLENCE JAZZ ENSEMBLE METHOD. The jazz tradition is rich and varied, calling many styles of music its own. This book will provide you with an introduction to understanding, enjoying, and performing this exciting music.

The book is divided into three sections, each representing a different jazz style: **Rock**, **Swing**, and **Latin**. The three sections are color-coded:

- ◆ The **Rock** section is indicated by tabs and graphics.
- ◆ The **Swing** section is indicated by tabs and graphics.
- ◆ The **Latin** section is indicated by tabs and graphics.

Each section contains RHYTHM STUDIES and IMPROVISATION STUDIES which may be played with other members of the jazz ensemble, or with the CD found on page 49. The CD track number for each exercise is indicated by a CD icon and number (for example: 5). Further information about the CD is included on CD track 1.

Each section of the book also includes compositions, or **charts**, that apply what you learn in the RHYTHM STUDIES and IMPROVISATION STUDIES. These charts are designed to be played with the full jazz ensemble.

As with any type of music, learning to play jazz requires hard work and dedication. Careful study and use of this book will help you develop the skills you need to become a fine jazz musician. The rewards are well worth it!

Best wishes,

Dean Sorenson

Bruce Pearson

ISBN 0-8497-5749-5

KJOS NEIL A. KJOS MUSIC COMPANY, PUBLISHER

W31TB1

Rhythm Studies - Jammin' With Charlie

ROCK PLAYING GUIDELINES

- Follow the marked articulation on each note. Play notes marked > long and accented, and notes marked ^ short and accented.
- Separate non-slurred eighth notes.

When practicing RHYTHM STUDIES with the CD, listen the first time, then sing and play the second time.

ROCK ♩=116-120

1

2

3

4

5

6

Improvisation Studies - Jammin' With Charlie

BLUES SCALE

B♭ Blues Scale

JAMMIN' WITH CHARLIE is based on the **12-bar blues**, the most common musical form in jazz. The **blues scale** is a good starting point when improvising over tunes based on the blues.

The series of chords that accompanies a melody is called a **chord progression**. The basic **blues chord progression** (or simply **blues progression**) is a series of three chords played over 12 bars. Any note of the blues scale can be played over any chord of the blues progression in the same key as the scale.

ROCK ♩=116-120

A

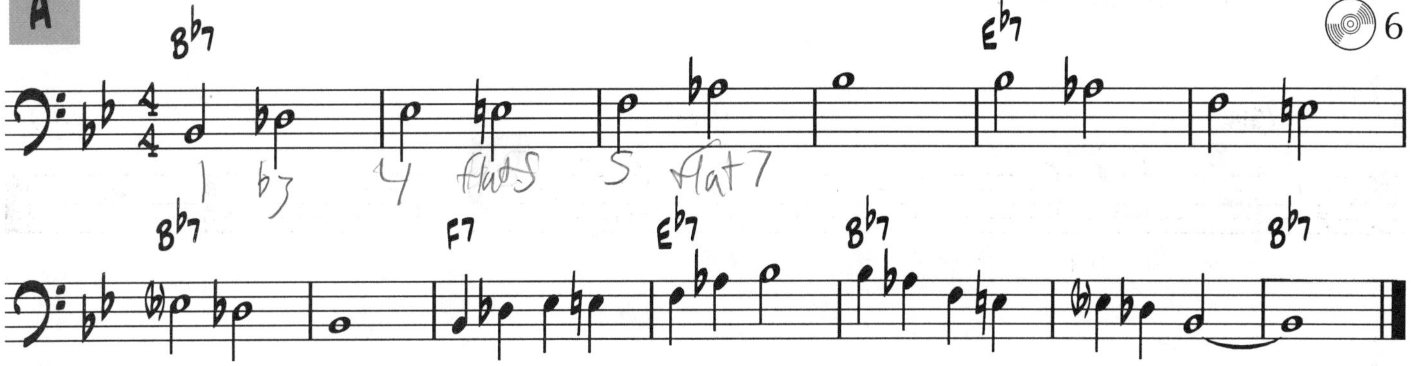

▶ The chords of the blues progression appear over the music in the form of **chord symbols**, a shorthand form of chord notation.
▶ As you play, listen to how each note of the blues scale sounds with the blues progression played by the rhythm section. Are certain notes of the scale more "bluesy" than others?

When practicing IMPROVISATION STUDIES B and C with the CD, listen and play both times.

B1

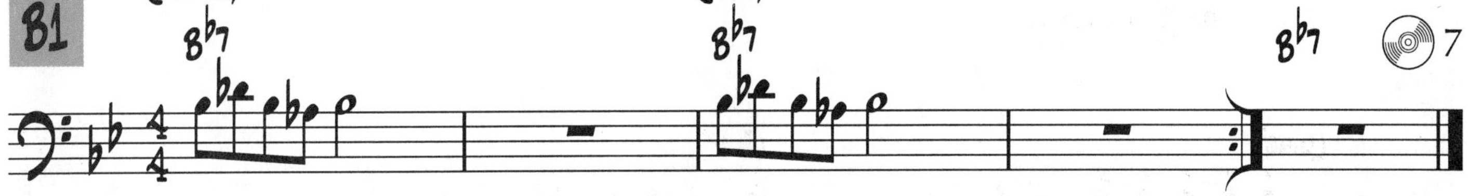

B2

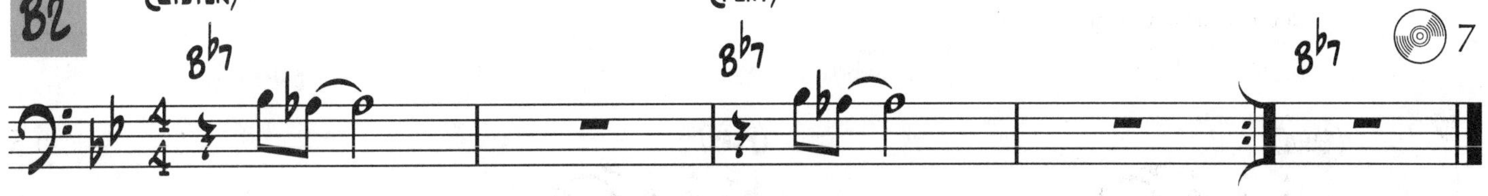

▶ These **licks** (melodic patterns) are derived from the B♭ blues scale.

IMPROVISATION STUDIES - JAMMIN' WITH CHARLIE, cont.

C1

(LISTEN) (PLAY)

C2

(LISTEN) (PLAY)

▶ These licks are derived from the B♭ blues scale.

D

(LISTEN 1ST TIME, PLAY 2ND TIME)

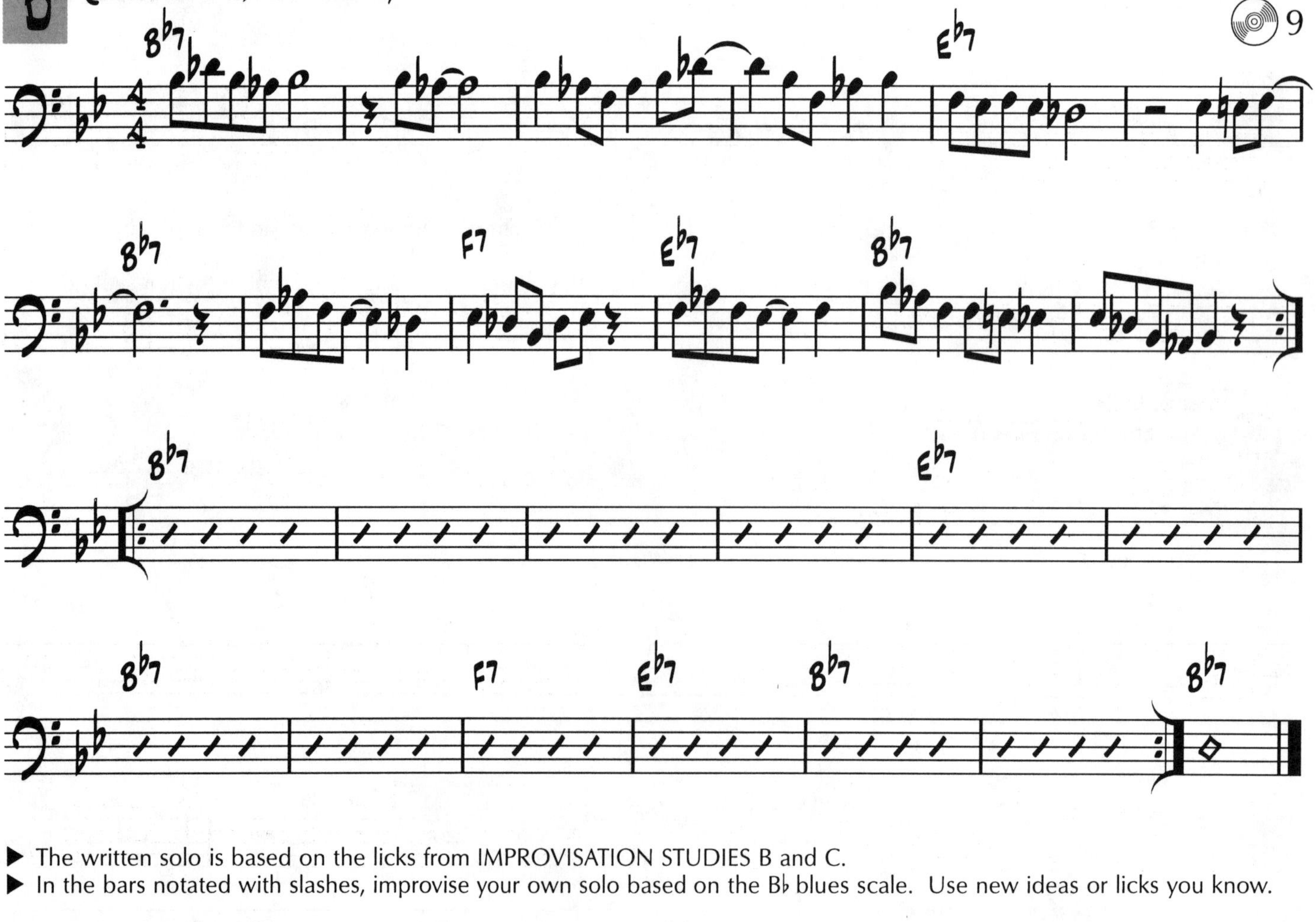

▶ The written solo is based on the licks from IMPROVISATION STUDIES B and C.
▶ In the bars notated with slashes, improvise your own solo based on the B♭ blues scale. Use new ideas or licks you know.

Jammin' With Charlie

Rhythm Studies - Uncle Milo's Side Show

ROCK

ROCK PLAYING GUIDELINES

- Punch (accent) all short notes.
- Play **on top** of the **groove** established by the rhythm section by mentally anticipating each beat so that attacks are precise and rhythmically accurate.

Rock ♩=120-126

1

2

3

4

5

6

7

8

IMPROVISATION STUDIES - UNCLE MILO'S SIDE SHOW

DORIAN SCALE

C Dorian Scale

UNCLE MILO'S SIDE SHOW is based on the **dorian scale**.

The dorian scale is a common choice when improvising over a minor seventh chord, like Cmi7 in the solo section of UNCLE MILO'S SIDE SHOW.

ROCK ♩=120-126

A

14

▶ As you play, listen to how each note of the dorian scale sounds with the minor seventh groove played by the rhythm section.
▶ How does the dorian scale differ from the blues scale?

B1

(LISTEN) (PLAY)

15

B2

(LISTEN) (PLAY)

15

▶ These licks are derived from the C dorian scale.

IMPROVISATION STUDIES - UNCLE MILO'S SIDE SHOW, cont.

C1

C2

▶ These licks are derived from the C dorian scale.

When you improvise, you are communicating ideas, just as you do when you speak. In improvisation, some phrases act as musical "questions," while others act as musical "answers" to the questions. Question phrases sound incomplete and unresolved, as if more is to come. Answer phrases offer a sense of finality or completeness. Skilled improvisers are masters at creating musical conversations that balance question and answer phrases.

D

(LISTEN 1ST TIME, PLAY 2ND TIME)

▶ The written solo is based on the licks from IMPROVISATION STUDIES B and C. Try to distinguish between the question and answer phrases.

▶ In the bars notated with slashes, improvise your own solo based on the C dorian scale. Use new ideas or licks you know. Strive to create a musical conversation.

Uncle Milo's Side Show

RHYTHM STUDIES - SPRING'S AWAKENING

ROCK

ROCK BALLAD PLAYING GUIDELINES

- Play accents with less force than in other rock styles.
- Sustain notes for their full value.
- Maintain the slow tempo without dragging.

ROCK BALLAD ♩=104-108

1 18

2 18

3 19

4 19

5 20

6 20

7 21

Spring's Awakening

Rhythm Studies - Martian Square Dance

ROCK PLAYING GUIDELINES

- Play on top of the beat to keep the **time** moving forward.
- Internalize the pulse to ensure precise attacks on syncopated rhythms.

ROCK ♩=128–134

1 (SING) (PLAY) 22

2 (SING) (PLAY) 22

3 (SING) (PLAY) 23

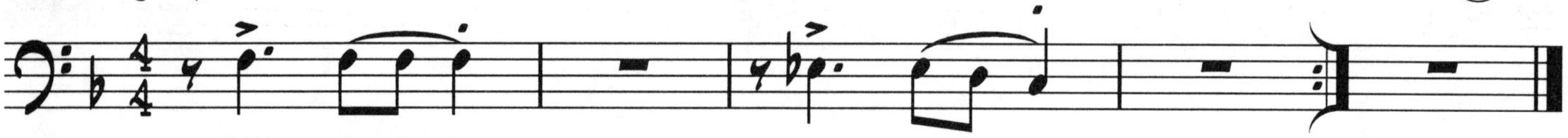

4 (SING) (PLAY) 23

5 (SING) (PLAY) 24

6 (SING) (PLAY) 24

7 (SING) (PLAY) 25

8 (SING) (PLAY) 25

IMPROVISATION STUDIES - MARTIAN SQUARE DANCE

MIXOLYDIAN SCALE

F Mixolydian Scale

MARTIAN SQUARE DANCE is based on the **mixolydian scale**. The mixolydian scale has some of the same "bluesy" sound qualities as the blues scale.

The mixolydian scale is a common choice when improvising over a dominant seventh chord, like F7 in the solo section of MARTIAN SQUARE DANCE.

ROCK ♩=128-134

▶ As you play, listen to how each note of the mixolydian scale sounds with the dominant seventh groove played by the rhythm section. Do certain notes sound better with the groove than others? Do some notes lead more naturally to the next note of the scale than others?

▶ These licks are derived from the F mixolydian scale.

IMPROVISATION STUDIES - MARTIAN SQUARE DANCE, cont.

When practicing licks, rely more on your ears than on the printed notes. Memorize the licks you practice and make them part of your internal musical vocabulary. As your vocabulary grows, so will your skills as an improviser.

C1

C2

▶ These licks are derived from the F mixolydian scale.

Finding a balance of notes and rests is critical to the musicality of any improvised solo. Skilled improvisers allow their solos to breathe and flow naturally by contrasting what they play with open space in the solo. Well-placed rests are just as important as the notes.

D

- ▶ The written solo is based on the licks from IMPROVISATION STUDIES B and C. Listen to how the rests allow the music to breathe and flow naturally.
- ▶ In the bars notated with slashes, improvise your own solo based on the F mixolydian scale. Use new ideas or licks you know. Strive for a natural balance of notes and rests.
- ▶ The C7sus chord is used to mark the end of each eight-bar solo chorus, and lead, or **turnaround**, to the beginning of the next chorus. Continue to use the F mixolydian scale when improvising over this chord.

Martian Square Dance

Rhythm Studies - Buffalo Head

FUNK PLAYING GUIDELINES

- ◆ Play every figure **in the pocket** by interlocking the rhythms you play with the groove established by the rhythm section.
- ◆ Feel a sixteenth note pulse at all times, even when playing longer note values. Internalize the pulse to ensure precise attacks, especially on quarter note and eighth note figures.
- ◆ Articulate groups of four sixteenth notes as long-long-long-short ("da-da-da-dut").

FUNK ♩=92-96

1 30

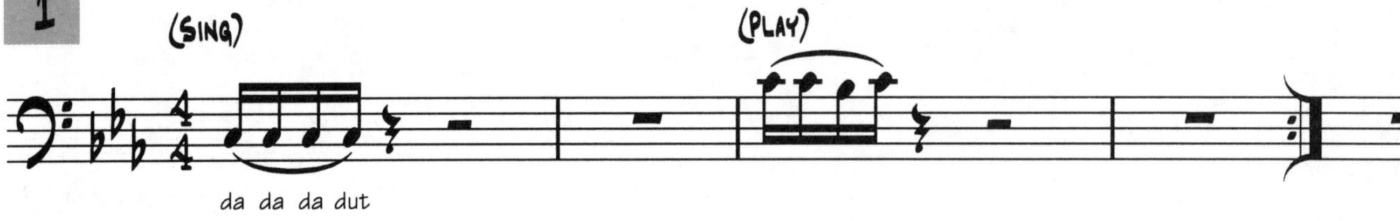

2 30

3 31

4 31

5 32

6 32

IMPROVISATION STUDIES - BUFFALO HEAD

NATURAL MINOR SCALE

C Natural Minor Scale

BUFFALO HEAD is based on the **natural minor scale**, also known as the **aeolian scale**.

The natural minor scale is a possible choice when improvising over a minor chord, like Cmi in the solo section of BUFFALO HEAD.

FUNK 𝅗𝅥=92-96

A

33

▶ As you play, listen to how each note of the natural minor scale sounds with the minor groove played by the rhythm section.
▶ How does the natural minor scale differ from the dorian scale?

B1

34

B2

34

▶ These licks are derived from the C natural minor scale.

IMPROVISATION STUDIES - BUFFALO HEAD, cont.

As you play licks and improvise, notice that simple melodic ideas have a pleasing musical effect. A solo need not be complex or extremely technical. Great jazz is created when the player communicates a message through a balance of notes and rests.

▶ These licks are derived from the C natural minor scale.

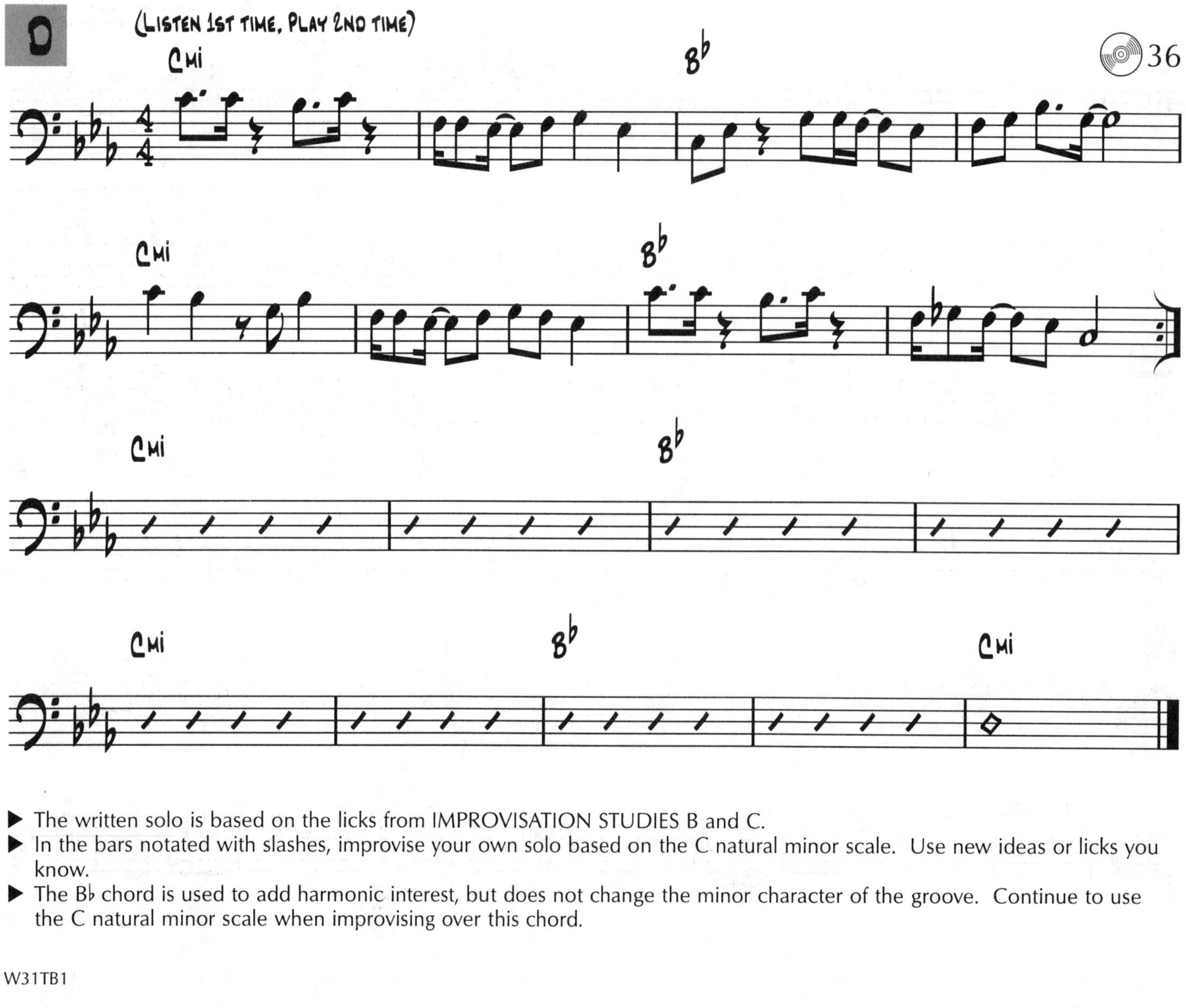

▶ The written solo is based on the licks from IMPROVISATION STUDIES B and C.

▶ In the bars notated with slashes, improvise your own solo based on the C natural minor scale. Use new ideas or licks you know.

▶ The B♭ chord is used to add harmonic interest, but does not change the minor character of the groove. Continue to use the C natural minor scale when improvising over this chord.

BUFFALO HEAD

RHYTHM STUDIES - MY DINNER WITH RONALD

SWING PLAYING GUIDELINES

- Mentally divide all beats into triplets. When playing pairs of eighth notes, the first note receives $^2/_3$ of the beat and the second note receives $^1/_3$ of the beat (♫ = ♩♪ triplet). This produces a **laid back** feel and is referred to as **swinging** the eighth notes. An eighth rest paired with an eighth note is treated in the same way (𝄾♪ = 𝄽♪ triplet).
- Follow the marked articulation on each note. Sustain notes longer than a quarter note for their full value, and release on the beat that immediately follows the note.

SWING ♩=120-126

1

2

3

4

5

6

7

SWING

IMPROVISATION STUDIES - MY DINNER WITH RONALD

BLUES SCALE

F Blues Scale

MY DINNER WITH RONALD is based on the blues progression just like JAMMIN' WITH CHARLIE, but in a different key. The blues scale is a good starting point when improvising over the blues progression in the solo section of MY DINNER WITH RONALD.

Knowing the blues in several keys is essential for any skilled improviser.

SWING ♩=120-126

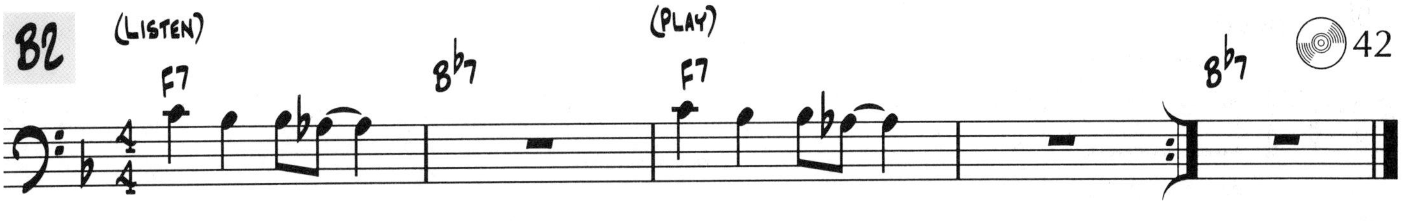

- These licks are derived from the F blues scale.
- After mastering these studies as written, try answering the first lick (B1) with the second (B2), and vice versa.

IMPROVISATION STUDIES - MY DINNER WITH RONALD, cont.

- These licks are derived from the F blues scale.
- After mastering these studies as written, try answering the first lick (C1) with the second (C2), and vice versa, or use the licks from page 21 (B1 and B2) as the musical answers to C1 and C2.

> Effective solos include a mix of both short and long phrases. Avoid excessive repetition by including this type of melodic variety in your solos.

- The written solo is based on the licks from IMPROVISATION STUDIES B and C. Notice how both short and long phrases are combined with rests to create an effective solo.
- In the bars notated with slashes, improvise your own solo based on the F blues scale. Use new ideas or licks you know. Combine short and long phrases in various ways and leave plenty of room for the solo to breathe.

My Dinner With Ronald

RHYTHM STUDIES - THE BLUES AT FROG BOTTOM

SWING PLAYING GUIDELINES

- Slightly accent every upbeat, using a stronger accent on the upbeat occurring at the end of a phrase.
- Mentally "play" the quarter and eighth rests within each figure.

SWING 𝅗𝅥=160-172

1

2

3

4

5

6

7

SWING

Improvisation Studies - The Blues at Frog Bottom

BLUES SCALE

B♭ Blues Scale

THE BLUES AT FROG BOTTOM is based on the blues progression in the same key as JAMMIN' WITH CHARLIE. The blues scale is a good starting point when improvising over the blues progression in the solo section of THE BLUES AT FROG BOTTOM.

SWING 𝅗𝅥=160-172

- THE BLUES AT FROG BOTTOM requires you to improvise at a fast tempo. In preparation, practice this study slowly at first, increasing the tempo as you become more proficient. Use a metronome with the clicks acting as **back-beats** (beats two and four of each bar).
- Try playing the B♭ blues scale in different octaves over the range of your instrument.

- These licks are derived from the B♭ blues scale.
- Practice these licks with a metronome. Begin slowly, increasing the tempo as you become more proficient.

IMPROVISATION STUDIES - THE BLUES AT FROG BOTTOM, cont.

When improvising, you can use the tune you are playing as a source of inspiration by applying pitch and rhythm fragments from the tune to your solos.

- ▶ These licks are derived from the B♭ blues scale and THE BLUES AT FROG BOTTOM.
- ▶ Practice these licks with a metronome. Begin slowly, increasing the tempo as you become more proficient.

When improvising at a fast tempo, it is often helpful to build the solo from short phrases. These may be derived from the tune or from the scale(s) associated with the chords of the tune.

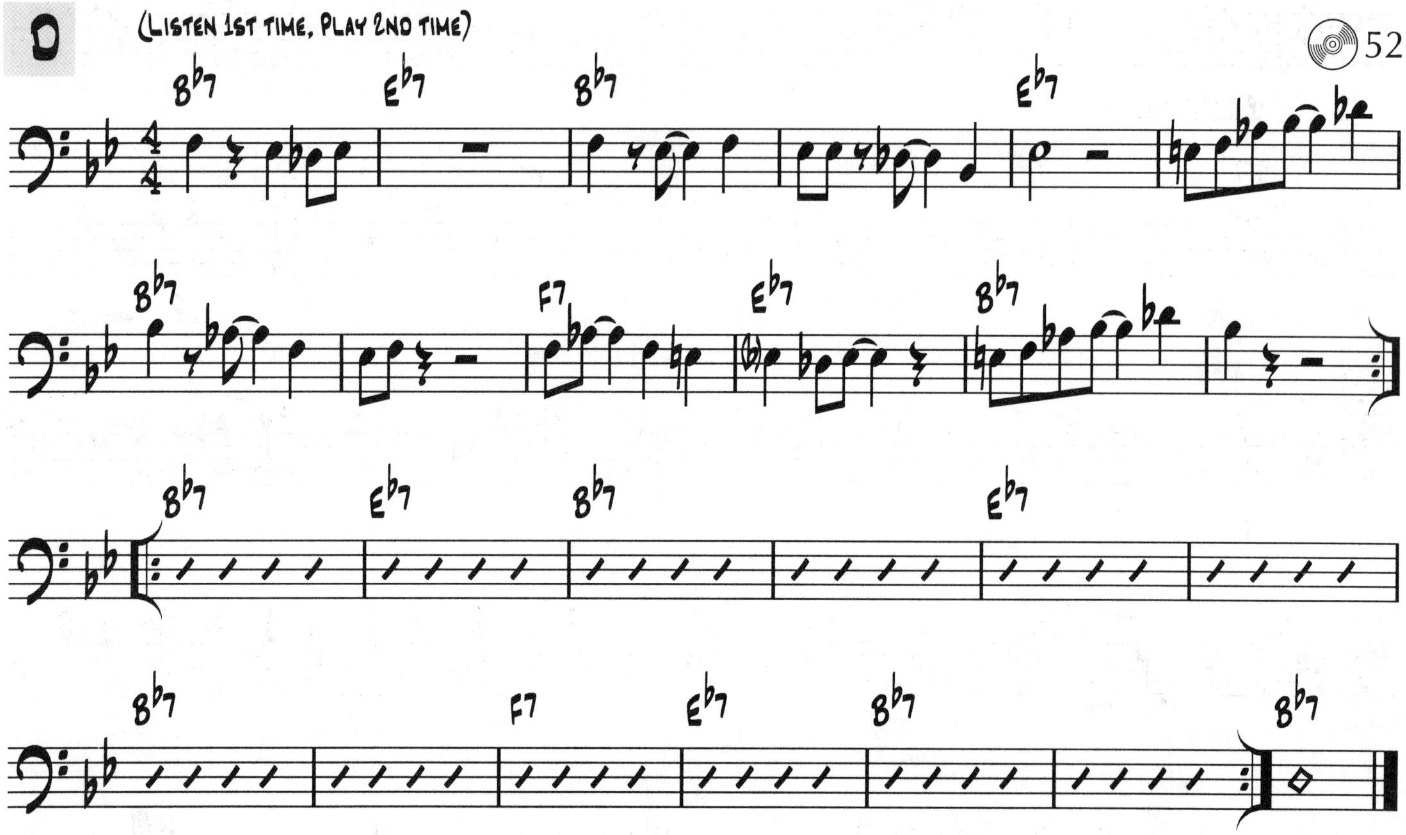

- ▶ The written solo is based on THE BLUES AT FROG BOTTOM and licks from IMPROVISATION STUDIES B and C. Practice the solo with a metronome. Begin slowly, increasing the tempo as you become more proficient.
- ▶ In the bars notated with slashes, improvise your own solo. Given the fast tempo, use short licks derived from the B♭ blues scale and THE BLUES AT FROG BOTTOM.

The Blues at Frog Bottom

Rhythm Studies - Last Dance

SWING BALLAD PLAYING GUIDELINES

- Maintain the laid back tempo and groove without dragging.
- Swing the eighth notes, exaggerating the triplet feel more than in faster swing styles.
- Accent upbeats, but with less force than in other swing styles.

SWING BALLAD ♩=80-84

1

2

3

4

5

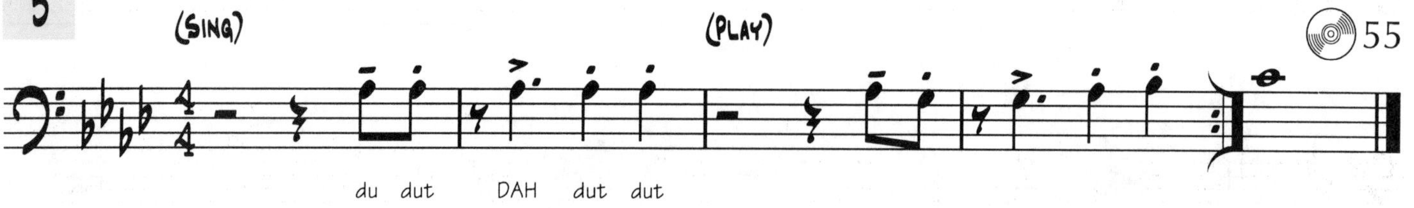

6

LAST DANCE

RHYTHM STUDIES - RIVER RAT SHUFFLE

SHUFFLE PLAYING GUIDELINES

- Swing the eighth notes, exaggerating the triplet feel.
- Approach rhythmic figures aggressively, playing on top of the beat to keep the time moving forward.
- Play single, isolated eighth notes short and accented.

SHUFFLE ♩=132-138

1

2

3

4

5

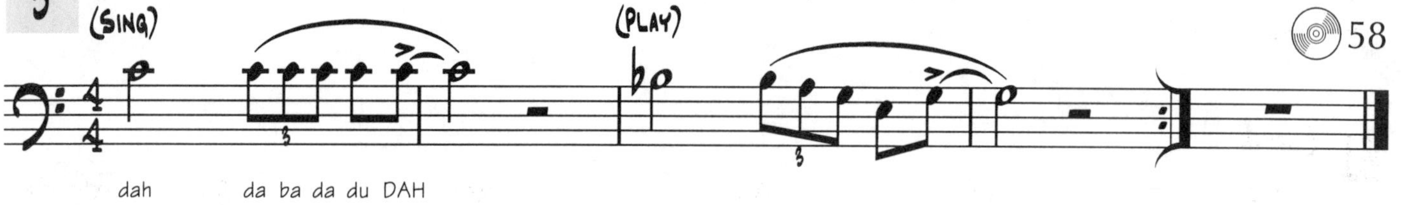

6

7

Improvisation Studies - River Rat Shuffle

MIXOLYDIAN SCALE

C Mixolydian Scale

RIVER RAT SHUFFLE is based on the mixolydian scale, just like MARTIAN SQUARE DANCE, but in a different key. Knowing the mixolydian scale in several keys is essential for any skilled improviser.

The mixolydian scale is a common choice when improvising over a dominant seventh chord, like C7 in the solo section of RIVER RAT SHUFFLE. The B♭7 chord alternates with the C7 chord to add harmonic interest, but does not change the C7 character of the groove. Continue to use the same mixolydian scale throughout the groove.

SHUFFLE ♩=132-138

When improvising, it is important to take into consideration not only chords, scales, rhythms, and tune melodies, but also the character of the music. <u>How</u> you play your solo is just as important as <u>what</u> you play.

Shuffles like RIVER RAT should sound gritty. The heavy back-beats, accentuated by the snare drum, give shuffles a raucous character that should be exploited when improvising. Play shuffle licks and solos loudly and aggressively.

▶ These licks are derived from the C mixolydian scale.

IMPROVISATION STUDIES - RIVER RAT SHUFFLE, cont.

C1

C2

▶ These licks are derived from the C mixolydian scale.

D

▶ The written solo is based on the licks from IMPROVISATION STUDIES B and C.
▶ In the bars notated with slashes, improvise your own solo based on the C mixolydian scale. Use new ideas or licks you know based on the mixolydian scale and RIVER RAT SHUFFLE. Strive to capture the gritty shuffle style.

River Rat Shuffle

RHYTHM STUDIES - WHERE DO WE GO FROM HERE?

JAZZ WALTZ PLAYING GUIDELINES

- Internalize the unique three-to-the-bar groove.
- Swing the rhythms, but minimize the triplet feel.
- Play on top of the beat to keep the time moving forward. Anticipate upbeats.

JAZZ WALTZ ♩=144-152

1

(SING) (PLAY) 64

2

(SING) (PLAY) 64

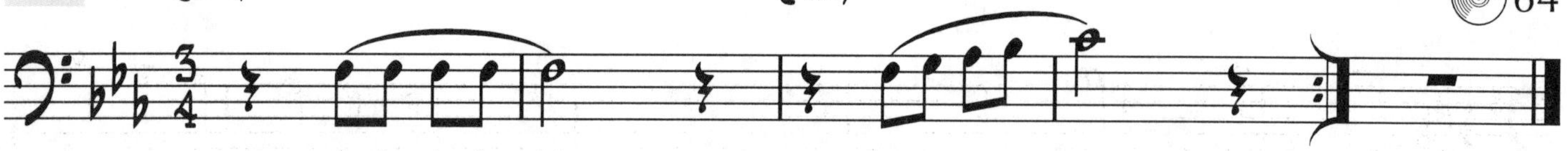

3

(SING) (PLAY) 65

4

(SING) (PLAY) 65

SWING

Improvisation Studies - Where Do We Go From Here?

DORIAN SCALE

F Dorian Scale

WHERE DO WE GO FROM HERE? is based on the dorian scale, just like UNCLE MILO'S SIDE SHOW, but in a different key. Knowing the dorian scale in several keys is essential for any skilled improviser.

The dorian scale is a common choice when improvising over a minor seventh chord, like Fmi7 in the solo section of WHERE DO WE GO FROM HERE?

JAZZ WALTZ ♩=144-152

A 66

B1 67

B2 67

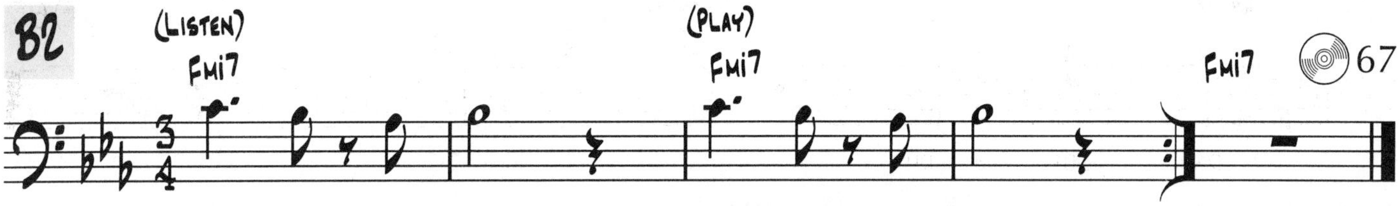

- These licks are derived from the F dorian scale and WHERE DO WE GO FROM HERE?
- Give yourself time to become comfortable with the three-to-the-bar feel. Internalize the groove through repeated listenings.
- After mastering these studies as written, try answering the first lick (B1) with the second (B2), and vice versa.

IMPROVISATION STUDIES - WHERE DO WE GO FROM HERE?, cont.

C1

C2

- These licks are derived from the F dorian scale and WHERE DO WE GO FROM HERE?
- After mastering these studies as written, try answering the first lick (C1) with the second (C2), and vice versa, or use the licks from page 35 (B1 and B2) as the musical answers to C1 and C2.

D

- The written solo is based on WHERE DO WE GO FROM HERE? and licks from IMPROVISATION STUDIES B and C.
- In the bars notated with slashes, improvise your own solo based on the F dorian scale. Use new ideas or licks you know based on the dorian scale and WHERE DO WE GO FROM HERE? Leave plenty of room for the solo to breathe.

Where Do We Go From Here?

RHYTHM STUDIES - SWING FEVER

FAST SWING PLAYING GUIDELINES

- Swing the rhythms, but minimize the triplet feel. Play the eighth notes straighter as the tempo increases.
- Lighten attacks and other articulations by using less tongue.
- Accent every upbeat, using a stronger accent on the upbeat occurring at the end of a phrase.

UP SWING ♩=172-200+

1

70

2

70

3

71

4

71

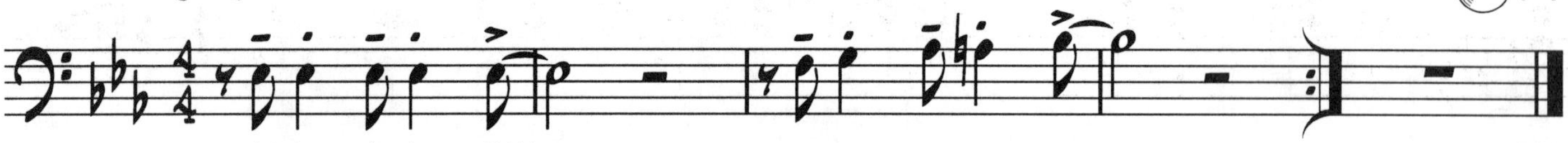

5

72

6

72

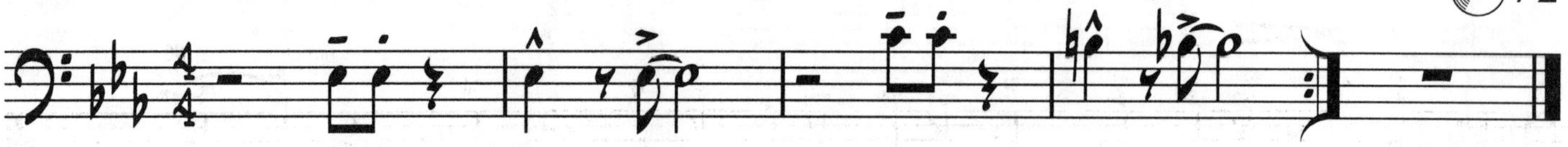

SWING

Swing Fever

Rhythm Studies - Bossa Madeira

BOSSA PLAYING GUIDELINES

- Play eighth notes straight, without swinging.
- Approach the rhythmic figures in a relaxed manner, especially when rhythms are syncopated.
- Where no articulation markings are included, follow swing-style articulation guidelines.

BOSSA ♩=116-120

1

2

3

4

5

6

LATIN

Improvisation Studies - Bossa Madeira

DORIAN SCALE

G Dorian Scale

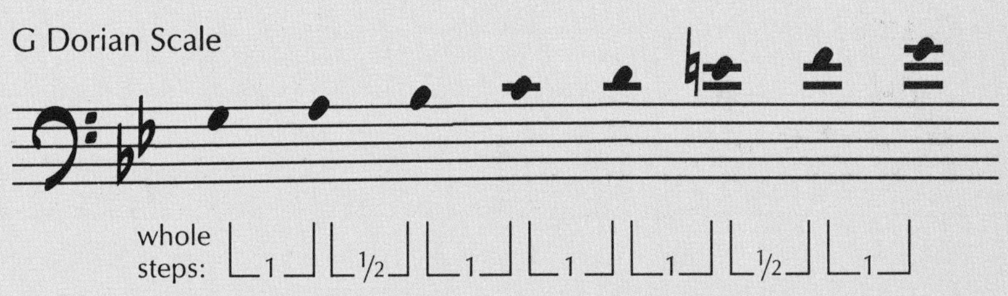

The solo section of BOSSA MADEIRA requires the use of the G dorian scale only, even though the chords alternate between a minor seventh chord and a dominant seventh chord: Gmi7 to C7. This chord movement from minor seventh to dominant seventh is called a **ii7-V7 progression** (or simply a **ii-V progression**).

▶ As you play, listen to how each note of the dorian scale sounds with the minor seventh/dominant seventh groove played by the rhythm section. Compare this to the sound of the dorian scale accompanied by a minor seventh-only groove, as in WHERE DO WE GO FROM HERE?

▶ These licks are derived from the G dorian scale.
▶ After mastering these studies as written, try answering the first lick (B1) with the second (B2), and vice versa.

IMPROVISATION STUDIES - BOSSA MADEIRA, cont.

▶ These licks are derived from the G dorian scale.

▶ The written solo is based on the licks from IMPROVISATION STUDIES B and C.
▶ In the bars notated with slashes, improvise your own solo based on the G dorian scale. Use new ideas or licks you know.

Bossa Madeira

Rhythm Studies - Into the Sun

REGGAE PLAYING GUIDELINES

- Play eighth notes straight, unless noted otherwise. (In reggae compositions, a triplet feel is sometimes appropriate.)
- Feel a half note pulse at all times, even when playing shorter note values.
- Articulate cleanly and crisply, especially on notes of short duration.
- Play on top of the beat. When a phrase crosses a bar line, imagine the bar line is not there in order to keep the time moving forward.

REGGAE ♩=88-96

1

2

3

4

5

6

7

IMPROVISATION STUDIES - INTO THE SUN

MAJOR SCALE

F Major Scale

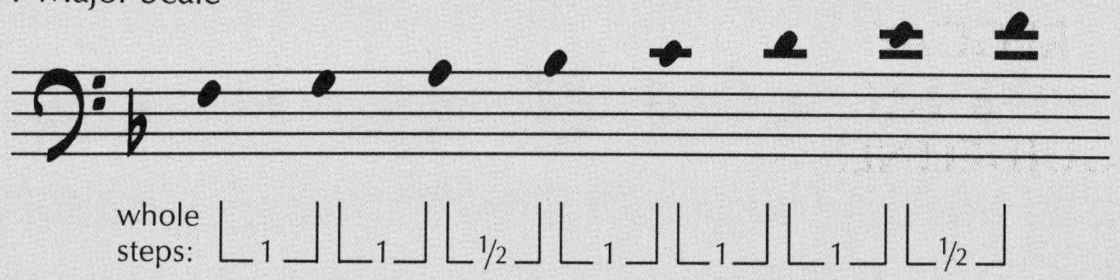

INTO THE SUN is based on the **major scale**, also known as the **ionian scale**.

Major scales are a common choice when improvising over major chords, like F and B♭ in the solo section of INTO THE SUN. The solo section requires the use of the F major scale only, even though the chords alternate between F and B♭.

REGGAE ♩=88-96

▶ As you play, listen to how each note of the major scale sounds with the major groove played by the rhythm section.

▶ These licks are derived from the F major scale.

Improvisation Studies - Into the Sun, cont.

C1

C2

▶ These licks are derived from the F major scale.

When soloing over a simple chord progression (such as the INTO THE SUN solo section progression), it is usually best to avoid pitches outside the scale(s) implied by the chord symbol(s). This is called playing **diatonically** or **inside**. When you <u>do</u> use many pitches outside the scale(s) implied, it is called playing **outside**. Always let your ear be your guide as to how inside or outside the chord progression you should play to create the best results.

D

▶ The written solo is based on the licks from IMPROVISATION STUDIES B and C.
▶ In the bars notated with slashes, improvise your own solo based on the F major scale. Use new ideas or licks you know based on the major scale and INTO THE SUN. Try playing both inside and outside, and compare the results.
▶ The C chord is used to mark the end of each eight-bar solo chorus and turnaround to the beginning of the next chorus. Continue to use the F major scale when improvising over this chord.

Into the Sun

Reggae 𝅗𝅥=88-96
mf
f
Open for solos
Backgrounds on cue
F
Bb
C
1, 2, 3...
...Last Time
fp
ff
Gradual Decrescendo
sub. ff

Warm-Ups

1 Long Tones/Tuning

2 Chop Builders

3 B♭ Blues Scale

4 F Blues Scale

5 C Dorian Scale

6 F Dorian Scale

7 G Dorian Scale